Staffordshire

Edited By Daisy Job

First published in Great Britain in 2019 by:

Young Writers
Remus House
Coltsfoot Drive
Peterborough
PE2 9BF
Telephone: 01733 890066
Website: www.youngwriters.co.uk

Softback ISBN 978-1-78988-696-2
Hardback ISBN 978-1-83928-031-3
Printed and bound in the UK by BookPrintingUK
Website: www.bookprintinguk.com
YB0412B

Foreword

Dear Reader,

You will never guess what I did today! Shall I tell you? Some primary school pupils wrote some diary entries and I got to read them, and they were **excellent!**

They wrote them in school and sent them to us here at Young Writers. We'd given their teachers some bright and funky worksheets to fill in, and some fun and fabulous (and free) resources to help spark ideas and get inspiration flowing.

And it clearly worked because **WOW!!** I can't believe the adventures I've been reading about. Real people, make believe people, dogs and unicorns, even objects like pencils all feature and these diaries all have one thing in common – they are **jam-packed** with imagination!

We live and breathe creativity here at Young Writers – it gives us life! We want to pass our love of the written word onto the next generation and what better way to do that than to celebrate their writing by publishing it in a book!

It sets their work free from homework books and notepads and puts it where it deserves to be – **out in the world!** Each awesome author in this book should be **super proud** of themselves, and now they've got proof of their imagination, their ideas and their creativity in black and white, to look back on in years to come!

Now that I've read all these diaries, I've somehow got to pick some winners! Oh my gosh it's going to be difficult to choose, but I'm going to have **so much fun** doing it!

Bye!

Daisy

Contents

Archer Ross (6)	85
Isaac Robert Hodgkiss-Fawcett (6)	86
Lyra Naomi Thompson (6)	87
Sienna Hyland (6)	88
Henry Mann (6)	89
William S. Manning (6)	90
Nancy Oliver (6)	91
Harry (6)	92
Lydia Lowe (6)	93
Alexander Robert James Briggs (6)	94

Hob Hill CE/Methodist (VC) Primary School, Brereton

Dylan Winter (7)	95
Caelan Leigh (7)	96
George Stokes (6)	99
Max Cooper-O'Dowd (6)	100
Hollie Flannery (6)	103
Isla Grace Cooper (7)	104
Hailey Wallbank (7)	106
Scarlet Gaffney (6)	108
Imogen Leigh Bennett (7)	110
Harry Thurstance (6)	112
Charlie Guy (7)	114
Liam Ward (7)	116
Demi-Mai Elizabeth Davis (7)	118
Amy Monaghan (6)	120
Joey William Ashurst (6)	122
Taya Stokes (7)	123
Thomas Perry Hayes (6)	124
Sorron Smart (7)	125
Leighton Evans (6)	126

Hutchinson Memorial CE First School, Checkley

Christopher George Ethan Minshall (6)	127
Ruby Rankin (6)	128
Sian Keeling (6)	130
Millie Brown (7)	132

Emilia Skinner (5)	134
Freddie Cottier (6)	135
Ben Armett (5)	136
Grace Rushton-Plant (6)	137
Libby-Rae Milson (6)	138
Fletcher Amos (6)	139
Ava Bromage (5)	140
Alfie Walmsley (5)	141
Jessica Spooner (6)	142
Mark Paulinski (7)	143
Eleanor Spooner (6)	144
Oscar Harding (6)	145
Holly Ede (7)	146
Bella-Rose Price (7)	147
Logan John Shepherd (5)	148
Jack Turner (7)	149

Priory CE Primary School, Trentham

Elsie Davies (7)	150
Hollie Ralph (6)	152
George RP Stephens (7)	153
Beatrix Townsend (7)	154
Rosa Bebe Stringer (7)	155
Zuk Furley (7)	156
Ayat Kamran (6)	157
Isla Eaton (7)	158
Maisie Croxall (6)	159
Poppy Morrey (6)	160
Maisie Elizabeth Mosiuk (7)	161
Leo Kirk (6)	162

Tynsel Parkes CE Primary Academy, Uttoxeter

Isabelle Walton (6)	163
Holly Graney (7)	164
Niamh Roberts (7)	166
Evie Smithard (7)	168
Isla Ashby (7)	169
Elsie Gallimore (7)	170
Layla Walley (7)	171
Kaitlyn Whitehead (7)	172

Kameel Malik (7)	173
Jacob Longmore (6)	174
Jenai Rose Flint (7)	175
Bethany Nicholls (6)	176
Harry Chatfield (7)	177
Fletcher Hargreaves (6)	178
Jackson Buxton (7)	179
Leon Furniss (7)	180
Freya Bradley (6)	181
Hollie Ellerby (6)	182
Corey Smith (7)	183
Riley Garner (7)	184
Isaac Smith (7)	185
Gracie May Jones (6)	186

Dear Diary

Early in the morning, I ate my porridge and it was my job to save Katy. I set off on my journey in my hot-air balloon but the wind was too strong for the hot-air balloon. The wind blew me like a washing machine. I saw a massive gingerbread house. It burnt my bottom because the smoke was red-hot. The wind blew me again like a fan. I closed my eyes but when I did open my eyes I was in a forest. I couldn't believe my eyes and then I saw a witch. I did not know if it was a witch or an old lady that was wandering in the forest. I saw seven trolls. My tummy rumbled so badly. I was starving and thirsty too but I still kept going. I was never going to stop until I saw Katy. I hoped Katy was alright. The wind blew faster but I was so excited.
Finally, I got to the island of dinosaurs. I saw Katy and she looked fine.

Evie Fowell (7)
Cheadle Primary School, Cheadle

Dear Diary

One sunny morning I woke up in my bedroom. It was the day that I and my family were going to the circus. Just then I went out of my bedroom and I saw a clown outside my bedroom door. Then I thought, *is he going to take us to the circus?* I just didn't worry about it so I got my breakfast, got dressed, did my hair and finally I did my teeth. Then I was ready to go so I woke my family. I played my iPad while I was waiting for my family to get ready because it started at nine o'clock but it was half-past eight. So I said, "Hurry up!"
But my mum and dad said, "No, it's only half-past eight."
I said, "But it's a circus party."
"There is no rush." So I forgot.
Finally, we were ready to go to the circus. Then we jumped into the car. Daddy was driving very fast. When we got there my tiger was so excited that he accidentally licked, it was gross!

2

I saw a clown, a gymnast and I saw someone doing art. I saw a really good man juggling.

I ate sweets and smoothies, they were really yummy. I had a blue packet of sweets. My tiger had a blue slushie that was bubblegum and I had a red slushie that was strawberry.

Just then the show was about to begin. First, it was the gymnast. The gymnast asked Tiger to go up the ladder with him and he asked me to hold the ladder for him. It was very hard because he was very heavy. Next was the juggler. The juggler was juggling eggs and one apple. Finally, it was the clowns. One of the clowns put a pie on another clown's face. Everyone in the crowd was laughing their heads off.

Just then my tiger fell asleep. He was snoring so loudly that everyone started to laugh their heads off again but this time it was worse because it made somebody be sick.

It was the end of the party. We got home and went straight to bed.

Harper Ruth Booth (6)
Cheadle Primary School, Cheadle

Dear Diary

Early in the morning, I set off and I was feeling excited but a little nervous but I knew I had to save Katy. So I went off. Down below I saw a wicked witch and a sweet cottage. I was a bit hungry, then I heard something roaring. I saw an angry bear, then I heard nine silly, funny dwarves. Before I went I saw windy, swirly trees. Suddenly the wind changed and it blew me away. From down below joyful, caring Santa waved at me. A happy elf said, "Good evening to you." Then an angry polar bear roared as loud as she could but the funniest things were the penguins. The beautiful thing was the snowy mountains because when the snow dropped it covered the mountains but I wasn't sure if I could see another polar bear.
Finally, I saw Katy stuck in a tree and a volcano, but is Katy okay?

Isabella Rose (7)
Cheadle Primary School, Cheadle

Dear Diary

Early in the morning, after my yummy porridge, I set off on my adventure. I felt very optimistic and excited. I said bye-bye to my grandad. So I set off on my adventure to the island of dinosaurs.

I saw an awfully lonely girl in a loud banging forest with a wicked witch. The girl was crying. I wanted to help her but I couldn't because I was busy.

The clouds turned grey and it started to rain. So I put my coat on and made myself some beans on toast and made myself cosy. After that, I saw another witch. I was eating the gingerbread off her house. After that, I saw a sweet candyfloss cottage but I wouldn't want to eat it all.

Soon, the clouds went bang and it blew me away and the temperature went cold. I looked down and I saw cold, colossal mountains that stood very still. I saw cute little penguins just diving in the icy pond.

Also, I saw a big beastly yeti. It was really scary. On the way, I saw tiny flappy penguins. There were fierce polar bears. The cold wind blew me in a warm, noisy place. *How far away am I?* I heard noisy cars driving. I smelt unhealthy air so I had to hold my breath. The sky was bright blue. There were loud dogs. It was going to be a great adventure. Teatime came but I didn't know what to cook. The only thing I had left was biscuits but Grandad gave me some money so I could go to the city to get some food. So I bought some more beans on toast.

Soon it was time to get out. I am finally here! It was a great day! I can't wait to tell Grandad what I have seen.

Ruby Elizabeth Plant (7)

Cheadle Primary School, Cheadle

Dear Diary

Early in the evening at 7:30 I was about to set off in my big, yellow balloon. I was trying to see dinosaurs. I was quite brave. I went through crashing trees and seven silly dwarves. I was scared because I saw a crooked witch. What an adventure it was! I wonder what adventure will be next?
That crooked witch nearly put a spell on me. *How long is it going to take me?* I went through forests and nice cottages with silly dwarves inside. I saw a cave with bears and wolves fighting. I was confused. I saw harmful trees that nearly touched the wolves and bears. How frightening those bears and wolves were!
Suddenly my balloon drifted away to the north. I saw helpful elves but they stared at me. One of the elves told Santa that I was in the air. It was calm and peaceful. I heard a howl, it was one of those wolves.

The polar bears were painful because they had got hurt so I went down and rescued the baby polar bears. I put air in my balloon again. I was cold because I'd forgotten my jacket and coat.

I heard a noise. What could it be? Suddenly my balloon drifted away to a city. It was quite busy and noisy. I saw planes, helicopters and paragliders. There were thousands of shops, I even saw churches. I thought I could land but I had to save Katy. Aargh! I nearly crashed into a plane but I was lucky.

Finally, my balloon drifted and I landed on the top of the water. I looked for Katy. I rescued Katy before the volcano erupted.

Nathan Lilleker (7)

Cheadle Primary School, Cheadle

Dear Diary

That day I set off I had butterflies in my stomach. I said bye to my grandfather then I went over the crashing seas. The clouds kept banging, it was rough! I could hear a small noise from the water like a sea monster under the boat. When I got to the forest it was gloomy. I felt safe so I calmed down. I went down and searched for Katy. It was dark so I could not see very well. I looked in the trees to find Katy. I checked in big holes for Katy. I looked everywhere. I went back to my hot-air balloon. I looked down, my belly dropped. I got scared. The trees were bendy, pointy and eerie. Suddenly the temperature dropped so I knew that there were mountains. *Why did I do this?* I thought. When I looked down I saw colossal mountains. I landed the hot-air balloon. The temperature dropped, it was cold. I looked behind me and there was a big, beastly yeti. I ran as quickly as I could.

I climbed up the mountains. I could not find her. Then I saw a polar bear, a daddy one. I was scared. I ran to somewhere strange. It was like Santa's workshop. I saw Santa and his elves. When I saw Santa it was surprising.

Then I tried to find my way back to the hot-air balloon. I felt ecstatic. Suddenly the balloon shook and I fell over in the basket. It was strong.

Finally, I saw a smoky volcano. I was finally there and I could see the island. I was waiting for it. I was desperate to see dinosaurs. I didn't know that they were there.

Tyler Harper (6)
Cheadle Primary School, Cheadle

Dear Diary

Early in the morning, I set up the hot-air balloon to save someone and I said goodbye to Grandad. He said to be safe and I said, "I will be safe." I was feeling brave and happy because I was saving someone.

The wind was stormy and swirly but it was just sunny, that was strange. If it was sunny, what had happened to the wind? What if I called for help? I could tell Grandad or I could solve it myself.

Then I saw a sweet cottage with seven dwarves. They were singing. Then I saw a wicked witch making a magic spell and she was horrid. When it was raining I was getting wet. I didn't like it. *Why did I not bring a coat?* I was mad because I didn't take a coat. I wished I'd got a coat, then a coat appeared in the hot-air balloon. I couldn't believe it.

Suddenly I got to lots of snowy mountains. I saw a beastly yeti on a snowy mountain but then snow was coming. I said, "What will I do?" Then an umbrella appeared. "That was weird," I said. Then I wasn't getting wet. I saw as well a beastly snow dragon and he was breathing fire out of his mouth. I thought, *how about I give the snow dragon some water then I can give the dragon the water, then he will not breathe fire.*
Then finally, I got to the island and I hoped Katy was okay. When I walked for a little more somebody called my name. It was Katy. She was in a tree.

Eleanor Clarkson (6)
Cheadle Primary School, Cheadle

Dear Diary

I set off at 3am with excitement and a goodbye to my lonely grandad and I said, "Have a happy time." I felt very optimistic and nervous. Then off I went. I waved at my lonely grandad. I came across a wind storm and the trees were as wobbly as jelly and I saw a cave. I saw a hopeless wolf looking desperate for meat so I threw some meat down because I thought it was hungry and it was only a baby. I heard something, maybe it was just a bat. I thought, *oh I hope my grandad is okay. I wonder how far it is?* I saw a sweet little cottage with seven silly dwarves wobbling down a swirly path. Suddenly I came across snowy mountains with a snowstorm and I was freezing but I was lucky I didn't get frostbite because I took a heater with me. So I sat by that heater, but not for a lot of minutes obviously just until it ended.

I saw colossal mountains and when I looked down I saw water with flappy penguins near it. I saw Arctic foxes hunting for meat. I saw an Arctic hare. Oh no! A snowstorm! But it went and I was fine. Then I saw a killer whale and a polar bear dancing on ice. That was funny! I saw a cave with a seal inside and when I came across a mountain I felt it was bumpy and rocky.

When the wind came the clouds were dashing like Sonic. Suddenly I came across Katy. We made a trail for the dinosaurs and went back to my grandad safely.

Olly Michael Tweedy (6)

Cheadle Primary School, Cheadle

Dear Diary

After I left my grandad I waved goodbye, feeling terrified. First, I was setting off on the awesome journey to save Katy. I thought I would never see my grandad ever again because I thought I would be eaten. What a scary journey it was! Just then a big forest appeared in the distance. In the forest, there was a fierce wolf pack and wide-eyed owls. But I didn't bother with the scary, dark forest, I just carried on moving. There were foggy clouds, dusty trees and scary animals. *Will Katy be okay?* I thought. Eventually, I saw a cold, scary place with snow-capped mountains. Underneath my balloon, I saw loud yetis making an awful roar. Snowy owls were tweeting and polar bears were prowling in the ice-cold snow. I flew over colossal mountains with freezing snow at the pointy tops.

Once, I went over a city at dawn. There were lots of skyscrapers and cars. "Will I get stuck in-between the skyscrapers?" I said to myself. I could see little children playing. What a big city it was.

In the end, I finally reached Katy's shipwreck and lots of trees. "Does my grandad still miss me?" I said to myself. What an amazing journey it was! I had finally reached the island of dinosaurs.

Jayden Mahoney (7)
Cheadle Primary School, Cheadle

Dear Diary

Very early in the morning, I got ready to go to a fabulous adventure so I got ready. I packed my lunchbox with a fruit salad and a sandwich. I couldn't wait to save Katy. At 6:30 I was ready to leave so I set off. Soon after that, I was in a deep, dark forest. I could hear an owl howling then saw it above the balloon near some grey, crashing clouds. The forest was made up of feathery, soft trees. Another thing I saw was a wide-eyed owl and the balloon suddenly moved on.

The view was all white because I was in the mountains. I saw cute, flappy penguins waddling around with fluffy seals playing with them. But sneaking up on them was a fluffy, hunting polar bear and far behind them was a bright polar bear den. Soon I was bored of the view so I hit my balloon and carried on with the journey.

Soon I was in a city and I could see 4500 cars and forty-nine houses! I could only see two people, one was walking its dog and the other was on a field.

I was really hungry so I got my lunchbox and had my fruit salad and the wind calmly blew me across. "Yes!" I shouted as I finally got there. Then I had my sandwich and fell asleep, dreaming about rescuing Katy. What an adventure it was!

Linda Snow Donadoni (7)

Cheadle Primary School, Cheadle

Dear Diary

Early in the morning, I set off at 7am. I got my yummy bowl of porridge. I was going to save a poor girl named Katie. I was excited, optimistic and a bit nervous. I was worried because my grandpa was old. Just then my balloon blew me away. Then I saw grey crashing clouds. I said, "What is that noise?" Suddenly I saw a bunch of seven silly dwarves. Although I was young I was still strong!

Then I saw and heard a white-eyed owl that nearly hit my balloon. There was a windy storm up ahead. When I was in the middle of the place I was daydreaming. A cute hare scuttled across the white, thick snow. Suddenly the wind blew me to a much colder place. Then right at that moment, I saw Elsa! Then jolly Santa was having a jolly time. Next to him was a helpful elf carrying some presents. I said, "What a helpful elf."

I saw beastly bears with loud voices. Then I heard lots of noise. I had to put my hands over my ears but my first guess was they were not happy!

The sky was blue as a bird. By half-past seven I couldn't believe Grandpa had let me go. It was so windy. The balloon went really fast. Then I finally reached it.

Ellie Baker (6)
Cheadle Primary School, Cheadle

Dear Diary

One sunny day, me and Jacob were walking along the path. When me and Jacob were walking along the path we met a tiger with orange fur. So Isaac came along and helped us to get the tiger out of the way. Then we went to Woodward Pottery. Suddenly a robber came and stole all of our clay!
The robber went in a rocket to the Speedway Planet. Me and Jacob went in our rocket. We reached the Speedway Planet and we saw a super speedway bike. We used the super speedway bike to get past the robber. There was a treasure chest, the clay was inside.
We went back to Earth. When we got back we went to Thomas Land. We went on Thomas the train. When we reached the station we had a party with an Xbox. Me and Jacob got sucked into the game. The game was GTA 5. We went on Concorde.

After, in the game, we met Alfie. Alfie said that he'd been sucked into the game as well. I said the police were coming. "Look," I said to the boys. "It looks like my daddy got sucked into the game as well."
In the game, we went to Los Santos Customs and we customised a speedway bike.

Flynn Woodward (6)

Cheadle Primary School, Cheadle

Dear Diary

When I set off late in the afternoon, I felt sick and nervous. I'd like to rescue a cat but this is better than rescuing a cat, I'm rescuing Katie.

I passed a forest that was a happy forest. I saw a stupid witch chasing some cute girls. There were tall thrashing trees and howling winds that blew me around.

Suddenly I felt cold. I saw jolly, fat Santa. I said, "Hi fat man!" He followed me with an elf and he hopped in my balloon. I saw cosy cottages, flappy penguins, cold ice and soft snow. He stayed with me for an hour and I had to say goodbye. I said, "Bye cute elf," as my balloon quietly and gracefully drifted away. I was in a jolly mood.

I saw hundreds of busy people and exotic little ones with loud dogs. I felt the smoky, unhealthy air and the bright blue sky blinded me. The busy people were dashing like Sonic.

Finally, I saw dinosaurs! I was there! Is Katie alive? I got my lunchbox, ate my lunch and then fell asleep.

Lottie-Mae Cartlidge (6)

Cheadle Primary School, Cheadle

Dear Diary

When I stepped in the balloon I felt sad.
When I left Grandfather I waved goodbye to
him. When I left Grandfather I was very
worried about him. "Don't worry
Grandfather, I will be okay."
On my adventure, I could see seals and they
were blue. Just then, I got to the forest.
When I looked down I saw lots of different
types of snakes. When I looked up lightning
nearly struck the balloon because there was
a lightning storm beside me. I thought I was
going to die and so I went to sleep.
When I looked down I saw an Arctic fox and
an Arctic bear. I saw a tornado. I was
scared of heights. In the distance, I could
see a town and some people saw me. When
I looked up it was raining and I nearly
crashed into the mountain. When I got to
the city there were lots of cars and lots of
buildings.

In a few days, I reached the island. When I reached the island I saw lots of palm trees. In the distance, I saw the shipwreck and the volcano. I had arrived.

Bailey Beardmore (7)
Cheadle Primary School, Cheadle

Dear Diary

When I left I felt very sad because I set off and left Grandad behind. What a sad day it was! In the hot-air balloon, I waved to Grandad.

I saw a teeny, small mouse when I looked down from the air and I saw a fox too on a tree by a river. Suddenly I found a stormy forest and it was so windy it nearly blew me out of the hot-air balloon. I saw something's footprints on the snowy floor.

In one hour I arrived at some snow-covered mountains. Down below, there was a big polar bear. He was trying to find some juicy fish. At dawn, I woke up at a beautiful big city. In two hours, in the distance, I could see the skyscrapers.

There was a volcano in two hours. What a long journey it was! Finally, I landed and I could see some dinosaurs. They looked as if they were going to fight me because they had blood dripping down their teeth and chin.

I felt really frightened when they wanted a fight.
How exhausted I was because I had had a long journey.

Charlie Cashmore (7)

Cheadle Primary School, Cheadle

Dear Diary

Early in the morning, I woke up. I felt very excited. I was ready for my amazing adventure. I waved to Grandpa, then I set off.

On the way, I saw a forest. Some hungry wolves were looking for food and I hoped they didn't spot me. Seven silly dwarves and a cackling witch were running down a wiggly path. Just then a blast of wind blew me. I ended up in the middle of the crashing sea. I didn't know why the sea was white.

Then I noticed I was at the North Pole. Two floppy penguins were waddling along. Three fluffy Arctic foxes were so fluffy they were like candyfloss. Just then a flake fell on my shoulder. It was snowing!

Then a flash of wind blew me into a city. There was a sign saying: *Hollywood*. A vicious raccoon and a shy puma arrived then lots of smelly gasses covered me. It was the noisy cars. Then a blast of wind blew me like clothes in a washing machine.

Finally, I got to the land of dinosaurs. I hope Katy is okay.

Anja Critchlow (6)

Cheadle Primary School, Cheadle

Dear Diary

Early in the morning, I ate my beautiful, spectacular breakfast and then I got set for my red hot-air balloon. I went to a different scene. It was windy when I went but I saw wicked witches that were on broomsticks. One wicked witch was naughty. I was scared because the witches might cast a spell on me. Then there was an awful spiky bear.

Then I went to a different scene that had flappy, shouting penguins and they were kind. The Arctic fox was so fluffy it was like candyfloss. Santa and his elves were there but I did not know if it was Santa. In the middle of the mountain, I saw an ice cave that was snowy and there was a goose but I was scared. I had a bellyache because I was hungry to death. Suddenly I was blown to another scene and it was an awful town. It was messy. It had crocodiles and sharks in the awful sea.

Is Katy okay? Finally, I had a sandwich because I was hungry. I saw a sunny and beautiful city. I am there now.

Milan Steven Chell (7)
Cheadle Primary School, Cheadle

Dear Diary

When I left the red and white lighthouse I waved to Grandfather as I flew off in my big red balloon into the distance. Katy was stuck so it was my job to go and get her. How scary it was! *Will Katy be okay?* I thought.

Firstly, I flew past a pack of fierce wolves and a sweet little house. How windy it was! The red balloon was being thrown about and I was feeling dizzy. Next, I came to a colossal, white mountain. I saw a big group of white, hungry polar bears. How amazing it was! *Wil the creatures in all of the mountains eat me?* I thought. When I looked up I could see the very, very, very wild, stormy cold and the red, white, big and brown balloon was being thrown about in the wild, stormy, cold, windy weather. "Stop! Stop! Stop! Stop!" I told the weather.

In the very, very end I came to the sandy, yellow, hot, big island of dinosaurs. I could see the brown ships so I hoped Katy was waiting.

Grace Fower (6)

Cheadle Primary School, Cheadle

Dear Diary

Very, very early in the morning, I waved goodbye to Grandfather. After that, Grandfather waved goodbye to me as well. Finally, I set off to the island. Then I got to a rainforest. When I looked down I saw some green trees and dead, brown trees. When I looked down I saw a big, rough, stony cave but suddenly I saw a scary bear. Then I saw the bear's full body, it was brown and big and a loud roar came out of the bear's mouth. What a scary bear that was!

The next day, I arrived at some white, snowy mountains but I nearly got caught on the pointy bit. How scary that was. When would I get to Katy?

The next day, I flew to a sunny city. Then I looked down and I saw lots of long thick buildings. But when I looked up a bit I saw birds. Then I looked to the side and heard birds tweeting.

Finally, I saw an island. But suddenly I saw a boat shipwrecked. It was Katy's brown boat. I had arrived.

Freya Brindley (6)
Cheadle Primary School, Cheadle

Dear Diary

As I left the lighthouse I shouted and said, "I love you Grandad." I was very brave and scared. I was very sad and happy. I was also very hungry and thirsty. What a sunny day it was! I was very scared in the forest because it was very spooky. I was very lonely and bored but I thought I could do it. I came to a noisy, cold forest. I flew across the cold mountains. I looked down and saw a hungry fox family and a hungry polar bear. It was such a long journey. I thought I was going to die.

In the morning, I saw some pointy, tall buildings and massive churches. It was very bright and I saw a beautiful island. I heard some shouting and it was Katy. I said, "What are you doing?"

Katy said, "Come down here."

I saw a bunch of dinosaurs and a massive volcano. Katy said they were the last dinosaurs on Earth.

Isla Elizabeth Townsend (6)
Cheadle Primary School, Cheadle

Dear Diary

When I left the red and white lighthouse I felt worried because I might get eaten by the tall dinosaurs. "Do you think I am brave?" I asked Grandfather.

First, I gently passed over a windy old forest. Underneath me, there was a hungry, wild pack of dogs. What a scary, wild forest it was!

One hour later, I saw the snow-covered mountains. Then I saw reached a big city at dawn. I saw the fast cars speeding to work and the happy children playing in the grand park. There were skyscrapers. I hoped I wouldn't get stuck in them. What a scary journey it was!

Finally, I saw the island of dinosaurs. I hoped I would soon land safely. I could see Katy. She was on a tree waving at me. She came down. Slowly, I saw a boat sink. "It must be Katy's," I said.

Gabby Pepper (6)
Cheadle Primary School, Cheadle

Dear Diary

One sunny morning there were trees. They were pink trees. I went to see them with my family. They were nice. They were different. They were like rainbows.

We had a family weekend. Then I found a fairy. I went to the zoo. My family was looking for birds and then we saw a unicorn. We were hunting for things. It was amazing! It was good, I loved it.

Next, I saw a fairy. I saw lots of things. It was nice and we had a picnic. I had jam sandwiches, it was nice. It was good.

Next, we went for another weekend as a family. We went to the fair. We had fun. I loved going to the fair. I loved going on the rides. I went on all sorts of rides.

In the evening we had a nice walk. I saw all fun rides. It was good.

Lilly Attwood (6)
Cheadle Primary School, Cheadle

Dear Diary

As I left Grandfather I began to feel a bit sad because I don't like leaving Grandfather. I thought, *I must save Katy! How did Katy get stuck on the island?* Suddenly, I found a stormy forest and it was windy. It nearly blew me out of the balloon's basket. When I looked down I saw brown twigs, wood and scattered brown trees. After a while, I saw snow-covered mountains with a snow fox climbing up one of the mountains looking for his prey. What a nice fox he was! Early in the morning, I saw some people going to work.
After a while, I began to fall asleep again. When I woke up I saw the sun rising.
Eight hours later, I saw an island. *What if Katy is on the island?* I thought.

Cody Davies (7)
Cheadle Primary School, Cheadle

Dear Diary

Early in the morning, I set off to save Katy from the smoky volcano and on the way I saw seven silly dwarves. Secondly, I saw candyfloss clouds and a wicked witch doing a wicked spell. On the way, I saw a quiet polar bear and its fierce daddy.

What a stormy day it was! What was in the forest? In the forest, I saw a pack of wolves howling or hunting for prey. Suddenly it went colder and the hot-air balloon was harder to steer. When I got where it was snowing. I saw colossal snowy mountains. On the way, I saw penguins diving in the water and coming out. I felt ecstatic because I wasn't scared of fifty dinosaurs. Finally, I saw the island that I was looking for. I hope Katy is alright and not hurt.

Zachary Griffin-Finney (6)
Cheadle Primary School, Cheadle

Dear Diary

One sunny day I went out in my hot-air balloon and I said goodbye to my grandfather. I felt sad when I left him alone. Grandfather said to be brave and he loved me so much.

I looked down and I saw horrible wolves. When I looked down I saw an Arctic fox. I got out of my hot-air balloon and I saw some trees going side to side. I got out of my hot-air balloon and I saw a snowy owl. Eventually, I got there and I saw a snowy polar bear. I looked down and I saw a snowman. When I looked down I saw a smoky house, it was very warm. I looked down and I saw a cold pond, what a cold place it was!

Finally, I got to the island and I saw Katy on the volcano.

Ruby-Mai Lovatt (6)
Cheadle Primary School, Cheadle

Dear Diary

One day I waved and said, "Do not worry, Grandad." I got goosebumps because I was scared. What an exciting adventure it was! I was too scared to look down and at the same time, I wanted to so I did. A fierce, frightening wolf tried to eat me! I did not know what to do so I screamed, "Help!"
In an hour, I caught a shiver. I knew something was cold and icky. I saw clouds of snow. I saw a white polar bear.
In an hour, I reached a city. I saw a huge skyscraper. I saw a huge lorry. Finally, I reached the island. I saw a volcano. It was about to erupt and I saw a yellow dinosaur. What an exciting day I had.

Sam Hayes (7)
Cheadle Primary School, Cheadle

Dear Diary

When I got up in the morning I was brave and optimistic to save Katy. I was going past cracking trees in the balloon. I could see rushing waterfalls with boats falling down. I saw dangerous wolves in a battle. I saw a wicked witch making a spell. The candyfloss clouds were glittery. The balloon moved on to the mountains. I got colder and colder because I was at the mountains. I saw beastly polar bears hunting for penguins. In the mountains, I saw a crooked cave. In the cave, I saw a tarantula. In the balloon, it was so peaceful. In the cold, I was freezing.

Finally, I saw the island. What a great adventure it was!

Kaiden Plant (6)
Cheadle Primary School, Cheadle

Dear Diary

When I set off at 3am in the morning, I was a little bit scared but I set off and then I got to the scary forest. There were windy tornadoes and they blew me around like a washing machine. I was dizzy but I saw bears fighting. I saw a flock of birds and I saw lots of animals. The wind came and blew me to the Arctic. I saw polar bears fighting fish and I saw a killer whale eating fish. I heard a wide-eyed owl and I saw a crooked cave on a mountain. I saw a pack of wolves eating meat. What will I do? What a nice place it is!
Finally, I got to the island because I could see a volcano.

James Elliott Mountford (7)
Cheadle Primary School, Cheadle

Dear Diary

Early in the sunny morning, I felt super brave when I stepped into the hot-air balloon. Before I set off, Grandfather gave me a yummy snack. Katie was in serious trouble so I needed to save her.

After a little while, I saw a wild wolf and a grumpy, beastly bear and trees going side to side. What a wild forest it was! After a while, I ended up next to the shivering snow-covered mountains. What a shivering place it was!

When the sun rose I drifted over the town quietly in the morning. What a quiet town it was! After, I was trying to work out where I was going to land.

Amelia Lillie Jean Ashgord (7)
Cheadle Primary School, Cheadle

Dear Diary

At 8 o'clock on a sunny morning, I built my balloon so I could get back faster. When I got in the balloon I was angry because I did not have anything. When it was the next day it was gloomy and the sky was black. It was raining but up ahead I saw some snowy mountains. I was getting closer and closer to the snowy mountains.

I was on the snowy mountains and it was cold. The snow was coming down and then I looked down because I saw a beastly yeti and penguins sliding down the hills. The yeti looked up and saw me. The yeti was chasing me. How far could he run?

Declan James Proctor (7)
Cheadle Primary School, Cheadle

Dear Diary

After my yummy porridge, I set off in the hot-air balloon to save Katy. On the way, I saw a gloomy cave and a fox. I saw a bendy, pretty tree with a huge owl with big eyes. Sometimes I got butterflies on the way because I ate lots of yummy porridge. Suddenly the hot-air balloon blew to the snow mountains. I saw two beautiful penguins jump into the ice-cold water. I saw an iceberg with two pretty penguins, a mummy and daddy. I saw a huge, fierce polar bear.
Finally, I saw a huge dinosaur eating flowers. I hope that Katy is okay.

Savannah-Jane Temperance Day (7)

Cheadle Primary School, Cheadle

Dear Diary

It was 10 o'clock on a sunny day, I jumped into the hot-air balloon. I waved goodbye to Grandad. I felt very, very sad because I never go away from Grandad. I waved to Grandad and Grandad waved back.
Where was I? First, I got to a forest and it was very cold in the forest. When it got windier and windier the balloon went side to side. *I must save Kate from the volcano and dinosaurs.*
When I got to the mountains it was very, very cold in the mountains. It got colder and colder and the wind got stronger.

Tillie Large (7)
Cheadle Primary School, Cheadle

Dear Diary

I went in my car in the school holidays to go to the zoo. I went to the zoo with my mum, my dad, my brother and my sisters. When we got there we needed to pay for a ticket and we went to see the lions. Then we went to get some food, I ate a burger with some chips and afterwards we had an ice cream because it was so hot there. After we went to see the monkeys and I saw rabbits too. I saw a tiger and an elephant eating an apple and another elephant eating a leaf. I then saw a crocodile and it frightened me.

Ethan Paul William Bird (6)
Cheadle Primary School, Cheadle

Dear Diary

One sunny day I went to the beach with my unicorn. Next, we got to the beach and made a sandcastle. We found a treasure box with money. Then we had some tea and we both had a picnic. For tea, we had mash, beans and fish fingers with water. After that, we played and danced with some music.

In the afternoon, we went in the secret tunnel and found a mermaid. She was crying so I asked her what was wrong. She said that she'd lost her dad.

At night, we found her dad. She thanked us and went home.

Tilly Walt (5)
Cheadle Primary School, Cheadle

Dear Diary

Before I got into the balloon I thought I might be able to get on the news! When I was about to fly away I waved to Grandfather happily. When I got into the balloon I felt brave, adventurous and invincible!
When travelling some bears pulled me down so I put some more fire in the balloon to get away. After that, I thought it looked like I was nearly going to make it... Then I saw the island but the wind was too strong for me so I put some more fire in the balloon. Finally, I got to the island.

Cameron Leese (6)
Cheadle Primary School, Cheadle

Dear Diary

Once there was a little girl called Sparkle and she was a little mermaid. I saw her at the beach and she was swimming in the water. Sparkle spotted me and then she said, "Hop in."
I said, "Wait a minute, I will just get my swimming costume on and then I will get in, okay?"
When we went home we went to get an ice cream. But when we were driving in the car we saw a dragon! The dragon was chasing me!

Bethany Lilleker (6)
Cheadle Primary School, Cheadle

Dear Diary

I went to the beach in the summer holidays and I went with my mum and dad and brother. I played in the sand and we played in the water and me and my brother splashed each other. We brought a football with us and we built some nets with the sand.
Then I played a game with my dad and my brother. After, we went to get some food. Me and my brother shared some nuggets and chips and my mum and dad had some steak.

Jack Rushton
Cheadle Primary School, Cheadle

Dear Diary

Once, I was very, very hot and me and my unicorn went to the beach. We went swimming in the ocean and we splashed all day long. But when it was bedtime the air was a thunderstorm. We were scared to death because there was a ghost. I went to the fairy world. As I went I saw Tinkerbell and we went to get a milkshake and we went to the park. After, we went to the shop to get make-up and our hair done.

Lilly Mae Davies (6)
Cheadle Primary School, Cheadle

Dear Diary

Once I woke up and I stood up and went to the park. I was going to get sweets, then I went to the park, then suddenly ended up in a forest.

I went to get my friends who are called Layla and Lucy.

I went somewhere with my pet dog and she is called Roxy. Suddenly she could talk so we went somewhere. We went to the church. My dog did do something funny and she did not stop dancing.

Poppy Hassell (6)
Cheadle Primary School, Cheadle

Dear Diary

I went to the farm centre on Mother's Day and I went with Mum, Dad and Tom. We were really excited and we had a brilliant time, then we went home. We had a snuggle with Mum and said, "Happy Mother's Day." We watched on the telly what Mum wanted to. She picked 'You've Been Framed'. We watched it all. Then we went to bed.

Emily Leese
Cheadle Primary School, Cheadle

Dear Diary

Once I went to the zoo with a monster and it was green with googly eyes that were yellow. It had three eyes and they were sticking up in the air. It only had two teeth with one tongue that was red. Its name was Yougo!
I was excited because there was a dragon there at the zoo and it had black and white stripes. The dragon could fly so high.

Alfie Pearson (6)
Cheadle Primary School, Cheadle

Dear Diary

In the holidays I went to a sleepover with my friends and my sister. I had some cake first and then some chicken and chips. I got there in the car. After food, I played with my friends and sister.
Then my mum picked me up and took me home. Then when I got back my friend left me a packet of sweets.
I will see you soon.

Lilly-Anne Jones (6)
Cheadle Primary School, Cheadle

Dear Diary

I went to the cinema to watch 'Dumbo' with my mum and dad and brother and sister. I went in the car to get to 'Dumbo'. It was a silly elephant flying, whacking everything over with the trunk and there were two mums and three dads and ten sisters. There was one little one and it was so cute.

Eden Milward
Cheadle Primary School, Cheadle

Dear Diary

On Mother's Day, I went to the JCB lake on my bike with my mum, auntie, uncle and cousins. I rode the whole way. It was a massive ride, it was 100 metres. After that, I was exhausted. Then I went to my cousin's house for a tea party. I had meat, broccoli and carrots and then we all had cake.

Bobby Barnett (6)
Cheadle Primary School, Cheadle

Dear Diary

I had my breakfast, then I got dressed and I went to the cinema. I watched 'How To Train Your Dragon 3'. I went with my family and it was a long film. Then I left the cinema and I travelled back home and I got my pyjamas on. Then I went to bed and on Mother's Day it was fun.

Jenna Walker
Cheadle Primary School, Cheadle

Dear Diary

I went to the zoo on the bus. I got there at 10 o'clock. I got some food first, then I went to see an elephant but it squirted water at me. I went to the gift shop at the end of the day to get an elephant pillow. Then I went home to sleep with it.
Talk again soon.

Jack Hughes (6)
Cheadle Primary School, Cheadle

Dear Diary

On a sunny day, I met a fairy with glittery wings, a wand and a sparkly dress. We went to get a milkshake. Where we went to was a magic unicorn cafe. At the door was a bunny and a dog.
I went to tell the girls. When I told the girls they were shocked.

India Blood (6)
Cheadle Primary School, Cheadle

Dear Diary

Today I'm going camping with my family and going to the beach.
I'm going swimming at the water park with my teacher. I'm going to the house with my dad and my family. I live in a hotel and it has a pool.

Jake Brookes
Cheadle Primary School, Cheadle

Dear Diary

One day there was a beach and unicorns lived there. The unicorn king and unicorn queen owned it. I was surrounded by unicorns! "Aaargh!" I said. "This is amazing! This is the most amazing day ever!"

Tabbitha Haines (6)
Cheadle Primary School, Cheadle

Dear Diary

Yesterday I went to a large war. I took down 10,000 men. My men were hiding in crates. The day before that day I went to the cinema to watch 'Puss In Boots'.
Talk to you soon.

Jack Mortlock (6)
Cheadle Primary School, Cheadle

Dear Diary

I went to the cinema to see 'Puss In Boots' the movie with my grandad. I went on my motorbike. After the movie, I watched another movie. It was called 'Kitty Softpaws'.

Danny Martin King (6)
Cheadle Primary School, Cheadle

Dear Diary

Yesterday I went food shopping with my dad to buy some food. After, I played with Rowan in my bedroom and we watched 'Steve and Maggie' and I felt happy.
Talk again soon.

Sienna Swinson
Cheadle Primary School, Cheadle

Dear Diary

I went to my nan's with my sister and my dad drove me and my sister at the weekend. It was so fun. I loved it.
I went to the cinema with my daddy, my mummy and my sister.

Rosie Weeden
Cheadle Primary School, Cheadle

Dear Diary

On Mother's Day, I went to Master Potter with my mum, nan and grandad.
On Saturday I went to swimming lessons. It was fun and I got there by Grandad taking me in the car.

Lily-Mae Coates (6)
Cheadle Primary School, Cheadle

Dear Diary

I got up and got dressed. After, we went to the park and I went on a run. I loved it. I had a picnic. Then I pushed my dad on the swing and then my mum pushed me on the swing.

Cole Keates (5)
Cheadle Primary School, Cheadle

Dear Diary

I went to the cinema and I went to watch 'Dumbo' on Mother's Day and it was good and serious. I went with my mum and dad and I went with my sister.

Annie Gregory (6)
Cheadle Primary School, Cheadle

Dear Diary

I went to Tilly's sleepover party. I went in the holidays, it was fun. I went in the car and Mum took me but she went straight home.

Roxi Estelle White (6)

Cheadle Primary School, Cheadle

Dear Diary

I went to the zoo and I went with my daddy.
I went at the weekend and I went in my car.
I saw a monkey and a zebra.

Jack Hill
Cheadle Primary School, Cheadle

Dear Diary

When I went to the fair I saw Hayden, Steve, Super Mario and Luigi. It was very fun because I found a football. Then we played with it. Mario was in goal so I had to always shoot in the corner because Mario can't go right, he always trips over. He once saved it then it bounced into a secret tunnel. Steve was very sad because he had to pick the football up. Then he missed his favourite lunch, slime meatballs. Luigi was very happy because he was number 10.

Ted Page (6)
Christ Church CE Primary School, Lichfield

Dear Diary

I want to be a fairy and I want to grant lots of lovely wishes. I like unicorns. I found lots of treasure. I want to go to Legoland. I like milkshakes. I want to be a unicorn.
I went swimming and I saw Mommy and Daddy peering over. I ate lots of lasagne at the weekend. I plated a game called Mario Kart and sometimes I won but not all the time. I played the Incredibles game and it is hard.

Poppy Nash (6)

Christ Church CE Primary School, Lichfield

Dear Diary

I went to the funfair with a unicorn and we played with slime. We went to the ice cream shop and got a milkshake. We went horse-riding at the funfair. After our horse-riding, we drank our milkshake. Then we did some dancing and gymnastics.

Then we went into the sea and met a mermaid so we carried on swimming with her. We found a pink shell so we kept it.

Matilda Isaacs-McCarthy (6)
Christ Church CE Primary School, Lichfield

Dear Diary

It is my birthday on the 28th of March and it is the 28th of March in eight more days!

Dear Diary,
I like Mondays because I go to gymnastics with Emily and I go on the bars. The bars are scary because they are high up.

Dear Diary,
I am going to see a fluffy unicorn! Mrs Leigh is very kind to me.

Jessica Smith (5)
Christ Church CE Primary School, Lichfield

Dear Diary

One day me and my friend went to the park in the afternoon. When it was night we were still there when another friend came. When they came we went home and played Pokémon and we found treasure in the game and we completed it. After the game was finished we went to the shops.

Samuel Wall (6)
Christ Church CE Primary School, Lichfield

Dear Diary

I went swimming with my cousin. I saw a mermaid in the water. She wanted friendship. When I went swimming the mermaid said, "Can you play with me?" I said, "Yes."
We played beach ball and sitting ducks.
After swimming, we went to KFC.

Amelia Craven (6)

Christ Church CE Primary School, Lichfield

Dear Diary

I went on my bike to Henry Mann's house and we went to the park together. Then I went back to Henry Mann's house and I had tea there. And after tea we had a little play. On Saturday we had a fun day. The grumpy person in my house was my brother.

Eddie Lester-Jones (6)
Christ Church CE Primary School, Lichfield

Dear Diary

I went to the zoo with my friends and a Pokémon too. I also went to the funfair and we did gymnastics and football. A monster was playing too. We did some art too and we had some lunch and played some computer games. I saw my friends outside.

Archer Ross (6)

Christ Church CE Primary School, Lichfield

Dear Diary

I went to the park with my friend. They are called Hayden, Joe and Tilly. Then I went to play with Dad at football with him. Then I went dancing at the competition with some friends as well. Then I joined with them. Then we went to the funfair.

Isaac Robert Hodgkiss-Fawcett (6)
Christ Church CE Primary School, Lichfield

Dear Diary

I want to be the snow queen so I can make the weather snow. I could make it always snow in a hurry!
There is a faun in a hurry. He is a spy. If people eat milkshake they are my spy. If they are on my team then they can eat terribly.

Lyra Naomi Thompson (6)
Christ Church CE Primary School, Lichfield

Dear Diary

I went to the zoo with my unicorn. I played
and at the weekend we made cakes. I
played games and I had lunch.
My secret is I have a real mermaid and a
real fairy. I ate chocolate and I had a
milkshake and I ate sweeties.

Sienna Hyland (6)
Christ Church CE Primary School, Lichfield

Dear Diary

I went to the funfair with my friends and it was really fun. But when I got to the funfair there was a tent and I saw a magician and the magician did some really good magic tricks. The best thing was ice cream with cream.

Henry Mann (6)

Christ Church CE Primary School, Lichfield

Dear Diary

One day I went to school with alien Harry and Bob the minion. We played football. I kicked the ball so high it went into space. Luckily Harry was an alien so he went into space and that game played on until it was lunch.

William S. Manning (6)

Christ Church CE Primary School, Lichfield

Dear Diary

I went to the fun park with my friends called Jessica and Poppy and there was a cafe. In the cafe they had a disco and there was food and drink. Then we had a party after the disco and it was fun.

Nancy Oliver (6)

Christ Church CE Primary School, Lichfield

Dear Diary

I went to the zoo and brought Joe, my best friend. We played football with my pet tiger and the tiger popped the ball. The dragon bought me and Joe a lollipop.

Harry (6)
Christ Church CE Primary School, Lichfield

Dear Diary

I went to the park with Jess the unicorn and we went to Candy World. We ate lots and lots of candy and an alien flew down into the candy world.

Lydia Lowe (6)

Christ Church CE Primary School, Lichfield

Dear Diary

I am a monster and I went to school. At school I saw my best friend. I played football with my family in the garden and I went to the zoo.

Alexander Robert James Briggs (6)
Christ Church CE Primary School, Lichfield

Dear Diary

Yesterday I had the most amazing day ever because I found a red crayon. I found out everything I drew came to life. I drew a door and I went through the door and it took me to an enchanted forest. I saw a sign, it led to a tiny house. I found out the tiny house was a palace. I went in the palace and I drew a carpet to fly on. I got on it and a purple bird followed.

I landed on land and I saw a purple door. I went through the door and it led home. I drew a bike and rode along. It started raining so I stopped under a bridge. I got off the bike and saw a door. I went through the brown door. Suddenly I went underwater on a squid. It looked like the carved squid on the bridge. When the squid landed I was on a rhino. I drew a seat to sit on. The rhino slowly went to a door to take me home. What a super day.

Dylan Winter (7)
Hob Hill CE/Methodist (VC) Primary School, Brereton

Dear Diary

Yesterday was the most exciting day of my life because I found a fire-red crayon and everything I drew came to life. I drew a door and it led me to an enchanted dimension! I wondered what would happen so I went in deeper and I came to a halt. It was a jetty. I decided to draw a boat and I drifted away. Very soon I fell down a waterfall. I quickly drew a balloon and floated off. Suddenly I saw a purple bird that had been captured. I saved it quickly but out of nowhere there were lots of terrifying people and they all grabbed me. They put me into the metal cage. Just then the purple bird gave me another magical crayon so I drew a magic carpet and quickly flew away to safety. I saw a purple door and I ended up in another city.

In the city I saw a small boy with a purple crayon. We both drew a wheel and created a bike so that we could cycle away. Soon we made a halt.

We saw a bridge that was crooked and made of old stone. It was weird because there was a door with a carved squid on the front. We looked at it mysteriously. It looked powerless. Bravely, I touched the door and it creaked open, I stepped in. With a shock, both of us were sucked inside the watery doorway and the squid came to life. It rattled and shook us until all three magic crayons were lost! Quickly but quietly, I slipped out of its grip and swam after the crayons. I grabbed them but they did not work because they were too wet so I rushed to the squid. I spotted a palace in the corner of my eye and next to it there was a science lab! I made my way towards it and quickly created a potion. I dipped the crayons into it and they worked again.

I went back out of the lab but seven fierce sharks were now chasing me and trying to eat the crayons. I quickly drew 1000 leeches. I blinked my eyes and in a flash, the sharks were swimming away.

I looked at the leeches and suddenly realised that their eyes glowed to show if they were hungry or not.

I was sad to leave the magical world but I knew we needed to escape, so I drew a large fish and the boy and I both climbed on. We went back to the magical entrance and the fish exploded. With a shock, a grey crayon landed in my hands. I wonder if someone drew the door with this? Would I ever find out where this magical world came from? What an exciting day.

Caelan Leigh (7)

Hob Hill CE/Methodist (VC) Primary School, Brereton

Dear Diary

Yesterday I had the most exciting day of my life. I found a scarlet-red crayon and I drew pictures with it because it is fun drawing pictures. Then I met a boy and rode off on a bike. We both had red crayons. When we stopped we were under a strange bridge. We went through the door.

When we came out we were amazed. We walked and walked and then we fell in the sea and there was a shark. We started swimming but it was too fast. Then a whale came. "That was unexpected," I said. The whale defeated the shark and we swam to the whale's back. Then the whale swam away. We felt shocked, I couldn't breathe because I was shocked.

It took ages to get home. I fell asleep and when I woke up we were home and we played on TT Rockstars.

George Stokes (6)

Hob Hill CE/Methodist (VC) Primary School, Brereton

Dear Diary

Yesterday I was on my way home but I saw a boy with a purple crayon and we drew a bike. After, it started to rain so we went under a bridge and there was a door with a squid on it so I opened it. Then we were swimming in the sea. I fell on a guard and all the guards were chasing me. Soon I lost the guards. I was in a castle. I looked in every room but there wasn't anybody in them. After that, I was at the last door and I found a boy. He wanted to go home but he was stuck in the castle. I ran to see the boy. I said hi and he said, "Who are you?"
I said, "What's the matter?"
He said, "I want to go home. I'm trying to find my way out of the castle."
I said, "Follow me."
The boy said, "Okay."

Suddenly the guards found me. I said, "Oh no! We need to hide because the guards are chasing me."

"We need to run," said the boy.

I said, "There's nowhere to run."

"What are we going to do then?" said the boy.

I had an idea. "We can run past the guards when they aren't looking."

"Okay, let's do it," said the boy.

"Run!" I said

"But the guards are still looking. When are we going to get home?"

Later, I had a better idea - to draw a whale so the whale could kick out the guards so we could run through them quickly and find the squid before they got back up again. After I drew a whale, the whale was stuck so I drew some water but the whale didn't know what to do.

At that moment, I told it and then it knocked them out, then we ran outside and we found the squid.
What an amazing day I had!

Max Cooper-O'Dowd (6)

Hob Hill CE/Methodist (VC) Primary School, Brereton

Dear Diary

Yesterday I saw a ruby crayon on my bedroom floor. I picked it up and I drew a magic door and it came to life! Suddenly I opened another door with a squid on it which was under a bridge. I followed the squid to a castle. Under the sea there were mermaids and mermen.
Suddenly the squid returned but a shadow came closer and closer. I drew a fish and it chased it away.
I went on a rickety bridge, it was a bit broken. Then I drew a rhino in a magical land with a rainbow but suddenly I got tired of adventures so I took a ride home.
When I got home the rhino went through the door. I went back downstairs and Mum and Dad were waiting for me. They said, "Where have you been?" I said nothing! Wow, what an exciting day I had!

Hollie Flannery (6)
Hob Hill CE/Methodist (VC) Primary School, Brereton

Dear Diary

Yesterday I found a scarlet-red crayon and everything that I drew came to life! I drew a red door. It led me to a fantasy land. If I went in, there could be a monster. The minute that I turned around I saw a boy. He had a purple crayon. We both drew a bike and we rode off.

Unfortunately, it started to heavily rain. We went faster so we didn't get wet. We stopped under an old bridge. I opened a grey old door. I carefully turned the knob quietly and opened it. It led me to a beach and we went swimming. Sadly we both didn't have swimming costumes! Then the boy drew purple trunks and then I had a red top and orange bottoms. If we went in the water was there going to be fish? Of course there were fish. So we went in the water, playing water tag. Then I forgot that I couldn't swim so I started to drown. What could I do? The boy was scared too.

Then the boy panicked. He could swim so he went in to rescue me. When a shark came the boy got me out of the sea and then I wasn't hurt. I was fine.

"Could we get ice cream now? I'm hot."

"Yes we can if you'll be good."

We went to get ice cream from the market and got strawberry and chocolate ice cream in the hot sun.

We got home on a hippo. When the hippo went we drew a purple, red and orange door to home. Then we carried on walking home in the hot sun because it was dinner time.

Wow! What an unexpected day I had!

Isla Grace Cooper (7)

Hob Hill CE/Methodist (VC) Primary School, Brereton

Dear Diary

Yesterday was interesting. I discovered a scarlet crayon. I felt amazed and shocked. Later, I was trapped in a humongous cage! Luckily, a purple bird brought my crayon back!

Five minutes later, I came out and I saw a boy with a violet magic crayon. We drew bikes and rode off. Unfortunately, it was raining so we stopped by a silver stony bridge. Then I pointed. "Look over there!" Just then we were teleported to another dimension but then we were teleported underwater. Suddenly we were grabbed by a massive squid! So I used the orange crayon. If I hadn't we would have been trapped there forever. Excitedly, I drew a castle but when we went in, the rug was moving. It was a little girl. She was frightened so I carried her on my back. Then there were 100 escape rooms! The escape rooms were terrifying and frightening.

"No one has been in there for 100 years," said the boy.

"How do you know?" I asked.

"I could smell it because I could smell the rust," said the boy.

How would we get home? Suddenly I had an idea. I whipped out my magic crayon and I drew a door. Then we were underwater again so I drew a surfboard to get to the surface. Just then I saw some guards in front of the castle. When we got there the boy drew a hippo so I drew a seat and we rode all the way home.

When we arrived home I felt lovely. What an interesting day it was!

Hailey Wallbank (7)

Hob Hill CE/Methodist (VC) Primary School, Brereton

Dear Diary

Yesterday I found a scarlet-red pen. I found out that it was magic. I drew a door and I put my hand where the handle would be. I opened it and I saw a magical world. It was amazing. I ran to a river and drew a boat. It led to a palace. Everyone waved at me. Suddenly I fell off a cliff. I drew a hot-air balloon. At that moment, I landed at a dark world. I got out and it started to rain so I saw a tree. I went to sit under the tree and I just saw a magic purple little door. I saw a purple little bird and he or she told me to go somewhere. It was a bridge and there was a secret door. I opened it.
Suddenly it led to an enchanted world. It was so, so amazing but we went on a dangerous bridge and I did see lots of missing pieces. I almost fell off the bridge. Suddenly I did not realise that there was another piece missing. I fell off the bridge.

The sea took me to a rainbow magical land. I drew a hippo and it took me somewhere. Me and my friend saw a bridge and we walked on the bridge but it had missing pieces. It was a good job we did not fall off. I had an amazing day.

Scarlet Gaffney (6)

Hob Hill CE/Methodist (VC) Primary School, Brereton

Dear Diary

Yesterday I had the most amazing day because I found a ruby-red magic crayon on the floor. Everything I drew came to life. When I drew a door it took me to an enchanted magic land. I met a boy and we drew a bike. We rode to a bendy, stone, sandy, broken, black, dirty bridge and it was raining there on the bridge. Suddenly we saw a doorway and at the doorway, I saw a squid on top of the doorway.

We opened it to an underwater land. Me and the boy had a snorkel, flippers and a helmet and we saw the bottom of a castle. Me and the boy went closer. We went inside but it led us to a bridge. Me and the boy finally crossed it. Then we came to a castle and we had a ride on a hippo.

I went underwater and saw a shark so I drew a megalodon. Just then I had an idea. As quick as a flash, I whipped out my magic ruby-red crayon and drew the biggest hole you've ever seen.

One by one we jumped in the hole because we needed to go home. We saw the bridge and we slid down the hole until we found the door leading out to home.
Wow! What an amazing day it was!

Imogen Leigh Bennett (7)

Hob Hill CE/Methodist (VC) Primary School, Brereton

Dear Diary

Yesterday was the most fun ever because I found a ruby magic crayon on the floor. Everything I drew came to life! When I drew a door it took me to a magical land. I met a boy with a purple crayon. We drew a bike but sadly it was raining so we stopped under a bridge. Suddenly we saw a door at the side of the bridge. I touched it and it took me to an enchanted castle. I was scared, I thought the guards would get me. Luckily they didn't see me. I was in an underwater ground.

Suddenly I was being squeezed by a squid's tentacles. Then it let go of me. I saw a shark that looked hungry. So as quick as a flash, I drew a megalodon. Luckily the megalodon scared the shark away.

Finally, we got to the big tower. So we slid down the megalodon's tail and thanked him and waved goodbye. I was relieved that we were safe.

What an amazing day but scary. I'm not going to use my ruby-red crayon again. What an amazing day.

Harry Thurstance (6)

Hob Hill CE/Methodist (VC) Primary School, Brereton

Dear Diary

Yesterday I found a cool, red and magic crayon. With it I can draw anything I want! In a moment, I drew a door and it came alive. When I opened the door it led to another dimension because I wanted to know what happened when I opened it! After my adventure, I met a girl called Imogen and we drew a bike. Unfortunately, it was raining so we went under a bridge. Suddenly we found a bullet belt with an orange crayon in it. Surprisingly, we opened the door. It led to underwater. Sadly we got eaten up by a squid! Sadly the inside of it was cyan. Happily, Imogen and I drew a super squid and spun out of the squid's mouth! Suddenly with a flash, I found two doors.

I said, "That's the door from earlier!"

"Yes it is," said Imogen.

We swam to it. In a flash, we made it.

"Finally," we said.

I wonder if we can draw ourselves.

Wow, what a supersonic day it was.

Charlie Guy (7)

Hob Hill CE/Methodist (VC) Primary School, Brereton

Dear Diary

I saw a magic crayon and everything I drew came to life. I drew a door and I opened it and there was a magic world. I was stood on the jetty. Next, I drew a boat and the boat led me to a palace and the guards said hello to me. Unfortunately, there was a waterfall. The guards were so worried.
Just then I drew a hot-air balloon. Suddenly I saw an airship trying to catch a purple bird. After that, they caught the bird and put the bird in a cage. I wanted to rescue the bird so I did. Sadly when I let the bird go the guards got me and put me in a cage just like the bird.
But then the bird came back and I was so happy and I drew a magic carpet and we flew in the sky. Afterwards, the bird led me to a purple door. I opened the door and the bird flew in. Next, we met a boy and we drew a bike and we both rode together.

Later, it was raining so we stopped under a bridge. It was the best day ever!

Liam Ward (7)
Hob Hill CE/Methodist (VC) Primary School, Brereton

Dear Diary

Yesterday I had an amazing day because I found a red shiny crayon. Whatever I drew with it came to life. I drew a door and it came to life. I went through it and it was so magical. I couldn't believe my eyes. It was like an adventure. It was amazing, I was dreaming. At the end of my adventure, I met a kind boy. We both drew a circle to make a bike and we both rode off together. It was a rainy day so we stopped under a stony bridge. I found a door under the bridge and on top of the door I saw a squid.
I went through the door. In the door the squid came to life. We went underwater and the squid let us have a ride. Just then the shark appeared. He chased us but we couldn't get away. Finally, we got away. I found a red crayon. Just then, the shark scared me and I dropped the crayon.

I found my crayon and I drew a door and it led me home. It was a spectacular day for me. Wow.

Demi-Mai Elizabeth Davis (7)

Hob Hill CE/Methodist (VC) Primary School, Brereton

Dear Diary

Yesterday I was amazed by what I saw. I found a magic scarlet crayon under my bed. I drew a door and it came to life! I was in another dimension. I met a kind, lovely boy and he had a purple crayon.

We both drew a bike and went under a bridge because it started to rain. I found a secret passage under the bridge. We both saw a carving on the door. I opened the door and it made a creak!

Suddenly a squid came to life. We swam with the squid. Unfortunately, I dropped my crayon. I was terrified. I saw a mermaid get it and she drew a bracelet. I thought, *will we ever get home?* I felt homesick. At that moment, the kind, lovely mermaid gave me my crayon. I was speechless and I said thank you.

Just then the squid came back and dropped us home. Suddenly we were on our bikes. I felt excited. What an exciting day I had!

Amy Monaghan (6)

Hob Hill CE/Methodist (VC) Primary School, Brereton

Dear Diary

Yesterday I found a crayon. Everything I drew came to life. I drew a door and it led to a magic castle. When I got home it was raining so I stopped under a bridge. I met a boy who had a purple crayon. We both went through a door under the bridge. Then there was another door but it was locked. The boy drew a key so we could unlock it.
Suddenly there was an amazing colourful sea world. We could see a baby and adult fish and an octopus who became our friend. It took us around the blue sea. After that, it took us to a mermaid but a shark was chasing me. We drew a magic, colourful, big rhino and he took us home. When the rhino was tired we drew a bed so we could go to sleep. What an amazing day that was.

Joey William Ashurst (6)
Hob Hill CE/Methodist (VC) Primary School, Brereton

Dear Diary

Yesterday I had an exciting day because I found a magic crayon. Everything I drew came to life. I drew a door and it came to life. I walked into it and it led to a magical land. I drew a boat. I got in and it led to a castle.

Next, I saw a pink coloured squid. Next, I was swimming with a squid and he took me to a magic land. It was called Candy Land. It was the best candy land ever in the world. It had marshmallows and lollipops, it even had chocolate ice cream. It was the best but I lost the crayons. I was so sad I was crying. Just then I saw them and I was so happy I wiped my tears away forever and ever but it was time to go home. That was the best day ever.

Taya Stokes (7)

Hob Hill CE/Methodist (VC) Primary School, Brereton

Dear Diary

Yesterday I found a red wax crayon. Everything I drew came to life. I drew a door and it came to life! I opened the door. I stepped in a magic palace. I came to a stop. Luckily as quick as a flash I drew a hot-air balloon and I saved a bird and I got caught. The bird saved me.

The crayon drew a carpet and I saw a dog. Then I saw a door and I went through the door and the dog followed me, but a squid tried to eat us. Then I drew a door and it led to a palace.

Next, I drew a rhino to take us to a bridge. Then we quickly opened the door. We were going home and we were playing. Wow! What a cool day!

Thomas Perry Hayes (6)
Hob Hill CE/Methodist (VC) Primary School, Brereton

Dear Diary

Yesterday I had the happiest day and I went to my bedroom. Next, I saw a red crayon. I wanted to draw on a piece of paper but I drew on the wall. After that, it came to life. I opened the door. Just then I went to a palace and met a boy and drew a bike. It started to rain and I stopped under a bridge.

Suddenly I went to the door and opened the door and on the other side I swam with a squid. Then I drew a rhino. After that, I went to the king but I heard a noise and it was a girl.

It was the best day ever!

Sorron Smart (7)

Hob Hill CE/Methodist (VC) Primary School, Brereton

Dear Diary

Yesterday I had a great time and I found a ruby-red crayon. Whatever I drew came to life. I drew a bear and it led me to a forest. Then I went to a castle and I met a boy. We drew a bike. It was raining so we stopped at a grey, strange, stony bridge. I found a door that had a squid on. I touched the door and it opened.
The squid came to life and the squid took me. I got away from the squid and then a mosasaurus helped me out of the water and took me home. Wow, what a great day.

Leighton Evans (6)
Hob Hill CE/Methodist (VC) Primary School, Brereton

Dear Diary

The most unusual thing happened to me today. I was playing on my Xbox when all of a sudden I got sucked into the game and I found myself as a character in Minecraft! I couldn't believe it! I was in my world in Minecraft, standing in my mansion. I went to the dog house to see my dogs, George and Peter. They were so happy to see me. I went to my safe chest and collected my pickaxe and my body armour.

It was going dark so I went to get some shut-eye in my bedroom. Suddenly there was an enormous roar from outside of my window! There stood the biggest T-rex in the world! He was hungry so I fed him some meat then he stopped roaring.

I went back to bed and in the morning I woke up and I was back at home. Was it all a dream?

Christopher George Ethan Minshall (6)

Hutchinson Memorial CE First School, Checkley

Dear Diary

Saturday 22nd December, 2018

Early this morning I woke up excitedly because we were going to Alton Towers' Santa's Sleepover. We gathered our things and got into the car.

When we arrived we got on a bus and went to the theme park. At the theme park we went on some rides including Spinball Whizzer. It was terrific.

After a while, we decided to head over to the Sea Life Centre to look at some colourful fish. We even stroked a starfish, it felt quite bumpy.

Later that day, we went to Santa's teepee and Santa gave us a present. It was a fluffy brown reindeer. We got some jingly bells and put them on the reindeer.

We then went for a rest in the hotel room and got ready for some delicious tea. After tea, we went to watch Alice In Wonderland the panto.

Soon it was time to get into my bunk bed, ready for another adventure for tomorrow. Bye for now, speak to you tomorrow.

Sunday 23rd December, 2018
This morning we had breakfast and went to Splash Landings. It was super fun! In Splash Landings there was so much to do. First, we went in the Lazy River and after we went outside to Flow Floods. I was shivering because it was so cold.
Next, we went into the warm Jacuzzi to warm up. It was really bubbly. Last of all, we went under the gigantic tipping bucket so we waited and waited until finally it tipped all on us, especially me!
We dried ourselves off while lazy Lola went into the Lazy River again! Soon it was time to head home so I said, "Goodbye Hotel." What an epic adventure I had at Santa's sleepover.

Ruby Rankin (6)
Hutchinson Memorial CE First School, Checkley

Dear Diary

Today I was so excited because I went to Germany to ski. I can't wait! We went in a van travelling to the airport. It was very big and silent because it was night. We had to be scanned and I beeped so was patted down. We met our family friends Maverick and little Valencia.

We got on the plane and it took off into the sky. Finally, we landed at Memmingen. We went to passport control and they checked our passports and let us through. We got a taxi to take us to the train station. We hopped on the train and it took us one hour to get to the village Fischen and waiting for us was Aunty Helene and Uncle Peter.

I had a sleep because I had been awake for ten hours.

We went to the ski shop to pick up my skis and boots for skiing and nipped to the supermarket. We were wide awake so we all went swimming with Mav and Val.

Later, we had tea and went to bed for a good night's sleep.

Sian Keeling (6)
Hutchinson Memorial CE First School, Checkley

Dear Diary

For ages I have been waiting for today because I am going to Willy Wonka's chocolate factory. But I don't really want to lose my golden ticket, although I'd rather go to the chocolate factory. Yay! We're going now. I wonder what we are going to see, smell, hear, touch and taste.

Dear Diary,
We walked through the big iron gates. As we walked into the factory we saw Willy Wonka. Willy Wonka has black hair and a big hat and I think he looks funny. The chocolate smell made my mouth water. The chocolate smelt delicious! Yummy, yummy! What a great day it has been. I walked around and watched the sweets being made. I heard the machines making chocolate.

I touched everything because I was curious. I loved walking around the factory.

Millie Brown (7)

Hutchinson Memorial CE First School, Checkley

Dear Diary

Today I saw a unicorn and the unicorn's name was Buttercup. Buttercup the unicorn came into school to see all the children and she met her best friends, Verity the mermaid and Daisy the fairy. The children wanted the unicorn, mermaid and fairy to do spells. The spells for the children were to make them fly with fairy wings and have magic powers. The unicorn said to the children, "We will go to my friend's house tonight to have a party. My friend's name is Jessica. I really like my friend. She is the best."
The headteacher came down the hall and told the unicorn to leave the school and to go back home with Verity the mermaid and Daisy the fairy. This was the best day ever.

Emilia Skinner (5)
Hutchinson Memorial CE First School, Checkley

Dear Diary

I went to bed on Saturday night. I went to sleep and I had a dream about a magical adventure.

I decided to go to the park with my best friend Jay and my brother Archie. So we got ready then went to the park. When we got there I saw a unicorn. Then I stroked it and it was like a teddy bear. I tripped over something so we dug it up. It was a treasure box. I lifted it up but it was locked. I couldn't find a key so I dug a bit more. Then I saw a sparkly key and it fitted in the lock. When I opened it there was chocolate and sweets and I shared them with Jay and my brother Archie.

Then I woke up and I couldn't believe my eyes and I shouted to my mum and told her about my dream.

Freddie Cottier (6)

Hutchinson Memorial CE First School, Checkley

Dear Diary

I am a footballer today. For my first time I played for Manchester United. I am a goalie and the colour of my shirt is light green. The crowd was cheering as we came on the pitch and then the other team came on called Chelsea. Four of Manchester's players were in defence, four were midfielders and two went out at the front. I went in the goal.

When the referee blew the whistle the game began. After fifty minutes I saved ten goals. All the supporters of Manchester cheered when I saved the goals. Then Manchester's strikers scored two goals each. It was the end of the football match. It was 4-0 to us. We won the match! It was my best day!

Ben Armett (5)
Hutchinson Memorial CE First School, Checkley

Dear Diary

Yesterday morning my maid woke me up very early.

She shouted, "Fire! Fire!"

I could smell the smoke. I jumped out of bed and I ran to the window. Looking out, I could see people running everywhere. They looked like rats escaping from a sinking ship.

Heart beating fast, I couldn't believe my eyes. Red, orange and yellow flames leapt through the air. The fire was spreading because the building was made from wood. Feeling frightened, I grabbed my clothes and ran out of the house. I knew I needed to save the great City of London. If London was going to survive then the king needed to save us...

Grace Rushton-Plant (6)

Hutchinson Memorial CE First School, Checkley

Dear Diary

What an amazing day! Today I went to my first football match. The day started at my nan and grandad's house. We had dinner and then it was time to go.
When we got there lots of people were there. They were singing and clapping, waiting for the game to start. We got to our seats and then I noticed there was something walking across the pitch. It was a black, brown and white cat. I said to Grandad, "We need to go and see the cat." When we got to the cat he came straight over. I called him Digger and he followed us back to our seats. Digger sat on my knee and watched the match.

Libby-Rae Milson (6)
Hutchinson Memorial CE First School, Checkley

Dear Diary

On Saturday I went to Stoke City Stadium for my first football match. Before the match, I went to the Stoke City shop. It was full of clothes. Then we went inside the stadium. I had a go on the mini-golf game and I got a hole in one. Then we got a drink and went to our seats. After that, the game started. Stoke had a great first half and had a few chances.

When it was half-time we got a drink and a sausage roll. Then the second half started. Stoke tried to score but they didn't so it finished 0-0.

We had a great day at Stoke City and I enjoyed my first football match.

Fletcher Amos (6)

Hutchinson Memorial CE First School, Checkley

Dear Diary

Today was an amazing day. I went to Candy Land on my own. I saw a sheep made out of marshmallows, trees made out of chocolate and mint and a park made of crushed Crunchies. I could not believe my eyes. All the chocolate smelt delicious and I wanted to eat it all up.

I thought it would rain water but to my surprise, it rained marshmallows. It was amazing. There were butterflies with bodies made out of chocolate and wings made from candyfloss.

Maybe next time I will take my sister with me. I had a great time. Goodbye Candy Land, see you again soon.

Ava Bromage (5)
Hutchinson Memorial CE First School, Checkley

Dear Diary

Today has been a sunny and rainy day. Unicorn and me were dancing in the soft summer showers. She was always a dainty dancer but when it was raining she was likely to slip. When she slipped she banged her head on a tree. Her horn fell off like usual.

Suddenly a fairy fluttered by. Her name was Starlight. Unicorn made her jump! She went straight to Unicorn and asked her what was wrong. She told her about her horn. Starlight used her magic wand while muttering a spell to fix her magical horn. She was so happy and began to dance again. What a busy day.

Alfie Walmsley (5)

Hutchinson Memorial CE First School, Checkley

Dear Diary

Hello, I am Tinker Bell! In the morning I had my favourite breakfast to help me fly. After breakfast, I got dressed in my beautiful green dress. I'm so small if I want to get to the top of something then I need to fly. When I first started to fly I wasn't that good so now I practise every day.
After lunch, I sprinkled fairy dust on my ten sisters. After sprinkling dust on my sisters, I took my pet dog to see my best friend... Peter Pan!
I was so tired after tea so I just went straight into my cosy bed. Sweet dreams everybody.

Jessica Spooner (6)
Hutchinson Memorial CE First School, Checkley

Dear Diary

On Saturday it was a sunny day so Mummy, Grandma, Eloise and I went to Consall Woods. We took a picnic. Mummy parked her car in the car park and I put on my wellies ready to go walking in the woods. When we were walking through the woods we picked up some sticks and we went to the bridge over the stream and we all dropped the sticks in to see whose stick would go under the bridge first. Then I walked through the stream to a tree that had fallen over the stream and climbed onto it. It was very bouncy. We had our picnic and then went home.

Mark Paulinski (7)
Hutchinson Memorial CE First School, Checkley

Dear Diary

Hello, I'm Spider-Girl!
This morning I had my Weetabix. I eat this every day to make me strong because I've got superpowers! My superpowers are... holding onto a rail, climbing onto the roof of a house and I can run so fast that no one can catch up with me!
After lunch, I had a rescue to go to. I had to go to a house because it was on fire! I couldn't believe my... eyes!
I was so, so, so, so tired. So tired I just went upstairs and straight into bed. I even forgot to get my costume off!

Eleanor Spooner (6)
Hutchinson Memorial CE First School, Checkley

Dear Diary

Today started with a visit to Pop Max TV Studio. I saw a Pokémon room and I saw a Pikachu. The Pikachu appeared on a screen and it came alive by magic. The Pikachu was yellow with a love heart tail. The love heart Pikachu was a girl. Some large speakers in the room began to play Little Mix and she then started to dance. The Pikachu's name was Pika. Then we started to dance with some props and play the piano. I then tried to go away but Pika followed me home.

Oscar Harding (6)
Hutchinson Memorial CE First School, Checkley

Dear Diary

Today we did maths, English and we saw a chef. We did English first. We learnt about apostrophes. I loved it. Next, we saw a chef and we learnt how to cook Chinese and we got to taste it as well. Last but not least, we did maths. It was a tiring day.
Then we got ready for home. Soon I was home and I had my tea. I then played a bit, then I got into my pyjamas, brushed my hair, did some of my homework, had a cup of tea, then went to bed and had biscuits.

Holly Ede (7)
Hutchinson Memorial CE First School, Checkley

Dear Diary

I went to the zoo. I saw some animals like lions, tigers and elephants. On my way home I saw a unicorn. I was so impressed I couldn't believe my eyes. I took her home. I named her Rose. She was amazing.
She had babies, three of them. One was called Esme, the second was Bella-Rose and the third was Anamia. Bella-Rose was good at being cute and Esme was good at being naughty. Anamia was very good at being nice.

Bella-Rose Price (7)

Hutchinson Memorial CE First School, Checkley

Dear Diary

I went to Twycross Zoo.
My cousin Eden came too.
We went to look at the tall giraffes and all they did was make us laugh.
Next we went and saw the monkeys, they were swinging on the trees and eating lots of leaves.
We went to see the leopards and they were running in their cage.
We saw zebras, butterflies, meerkats and many more animals.
I had the best time at Twycross Zoo.

Logan John Shepherd (5)
Hutchinson Memorial CE First School, Checkley

Dear Diary

On Monday I went to the park and you'll never guess what I saw. I saw a sparkly pink unicorn and it was shooting lasers out of its mouth. It destroyed the whole of the park. Some builders came to fix it.
Whilst it was being fixed I went to the fair. This time I saw a monster and it was buying a hot dog. I asked him if he wanted to go on the roller coaster and he said yes. We had a great day.

Jack Turner (7)

Hutchinson Memorial CE First School, Checkley

Dear Diary

I woke up in the sunny morning full of happiness. I wondered what was at the funfair today. How incredible!

Excitedly in the afternoon, my friend came and then a unicorn came into my room! How amazing! All of us zoomed to the funfair.

We landed in a bumper car and we bumped and bumped and bumped until the ride stopped. Next, we went on the aeroplanes. I was on the mermaid one, my friend was on the horse one and the unicorn went on the unicorn one! What a shock!

Then she said, "We need to go."

But I said, "Can we go on one more thing?"

"Yes!" Unicorn said.

So we went on the wheel. When we got off we were spinning.

"Now we can go," we said to the unicorn. It was amazing.

Elsie Davies (7)

Priory CE Primary School, Trentham

Dear Diary

I woke up in the morning full of excitement.
I wondered all about what the funfair would
have in store. How exciting!
Excitedly in the afternoon, I went to the
amazing, joyful funfair and I went with my
family. It was going to be the best day ever!
I could just feel it. What an amazing
experience!
I prepared a picnic full of delicious treats
such as chewy, delicious sweets, juicy, round
grapes and lots of yummy sandwiches that
were full of delicious fillings.
When I got to my family at 2 o'clock I rode
quickly through the streets, zooming past
the tall houses. We floated in the distance
and before my eyes, I could see the most
amazing funfair.

Hollie Ralph (6)
Priory CE Primary School, Trentham

Dear Diary

I woke up in the morning full of wonder. I dreamed about the funfair in town. How wonderful.

Excitedly in the afternoon, I went to the special, joyful funfair and I went riding my special motorbike. It was going to be the best day ever. I could just feel it. What an amazing experience!

I prepared a picnic full of delicious treats such as chewy, delicious sweets, juicy, round grapes and lots of yummy sandwiches that were full of delicious fillings. When I got on my motorbike at 2 o'clock I rode quickly through the streets, zooming past the tall houses.

This was actually the best day of this diary to date.

George RP Stephens (7)
Priory CE Primary School, Trentham

Dear Diary

I woke up in the morning full of happiness. I wondered all about what the funfair would have in store. How fun! Happily, in the afternoon, I went to the fantastic, magnificent funfair and I went riding my glittery, magical unicorn. It was going to be the most incredible day ever, I could just feel it. What an amazing experience.

I prepared a delicious picnic full of tasty sandwiches, yummy sausage rolls and chewy, delicious sweets.

When I got onto my unicorn at 2 o'clock I rode quickly through the streets, zooming around the large houses. We floated in the distance.

Beatrix Townsend (7)
Priory CE Primary School, Trentham

Dear Diary

I woke up in the morning feeling excited because I was going to Brumpton Museum with my mum and my friends.

Firstly, I went in the sandpit and then we went to a table with colouring and we made bookmarks. Then we went to see the birds and then we went in the car.

After the car ride, we went to a park and I went on the swings and then I had a healthy snack and then Poppy came to my house for a sleepover. Me and Poppy and the kittens went to sleep.

I will never forget my exciting day in 2019.

Rosa Bebe Stringer (7)

Priory CE Primary School, Trentham

Dear Diary

I once went to school with a monster. On Tuesday and on his first day he ate his maths book because he thought it was food. In science he drank the chemicals in biology, chemistry and physics. In English he wrote in Spanish so he could trick his teacher so she couldn't read it. That day was a little bit crazy but I better not go because my mum wanted me to make a video.

I think I'd better go now so goodbye for now. I will write soon.

Zak Farley (7)
Priory CE Primary School, Trentham

Dear Diary

One day I was at school and I came with my family and we had so much fun at school because we could go outside to play with our friends and play on the equipment. The equipment is the swings and the slides and the climbing things and we are very lucky because we also have some bars in different sizes and you can do anything on them like flips.

Ayat Kamran (6)
Priory CE Primary School, Trentham

Dear Diary

One day I was at the park with my family and we had so much fun and we saw some people that were funny. We went on everything at the playground, even the swings and climbing frames. I went on the slide and I went in the sandpit and played with the ball. I made a sandcastle. I went on the tyres with my family and I went on the bridge.

Isla Eaton (7)
Priory CE Primary School, Trentham

Dear Diary

On Sunday my family went to a funfair. My favourite ride was the Waltzers. Then I got to stroke a lamb and feed it as well.
On Saturday I went on the trampoline with my brother. We played catch with each other.
On Monday we went to school.

Maisie Croxall (6)
Priory CE Primary School, Trentham

Dear Diary

I went to the beach in Wales and I saw some shells and I went for a swim. Then I got dry and went back to the caravan and had a hot chocolate.

Next, I went to the arcade and played lots of games. Then I went home and I went to bed.

Poppy Morrey (6)

Priory CE Primary School, Trentham

Dear Diary

I woke up in the morning full of joy, ready for school. I got dressed and had my breakfast. After that, I brushed my teeth and went to school.

At school I did maths, EGPS and English. It was amazing. At the end, I went home.

Maisie Elizabeth Mosiuk (7)
Priory CE Primary School, Trentham

Dear Diary

One day I went to the fair and went on a very scary ride. I went on a train ride and I went on a steam and bubble ride with my dad. My mum, nan and brother watched me and Dad.

Leo Kirk (6)
Priory CE Primary School, Trentham

Dear Diary

Yesterday I went to the funfair with my unicorn pet, my family and my friends. We all went on the Ferris wheel. We all went to get some candyfloss but my unicorn didn't have ordinary candyfloss, it had unicorn, sparkly candyfloss. Me and my family and friends were shocked! We all wanted the unicorn, sparkly, glittery candyfloss but I said, "Wait, do not eat it because we will be sick."

My family and friends didn't believe me and started to eat it and I said, "Your choice." Then my family and friends felt funny. Then they were sick but not ordinary sick, that is just green, it was rainbow, unicorn, glittery sick. I was shocked again so I ate the candyfloss and I felt funny and was sick. Then we stopped. Then we went back home.

Isabelle Walton (6)
Tynsel Parkes CE Primary Academy, Uttoxeter

Dear Diary

I woke up and I was so excited because I was going to the beach! I had thought it was going to be an ordinary day until my dad told me I was going to the beach.
First, we got in the car and drove to the beach. My friend Isla came with me and we played I-spy in the car while we were going there. It was a long way, that's why.
Then we finally arrived at the beach. Me and Isla could feel the cold sea on our toes. We also had a paddle in the sea and my dad joined in as well. This is what the secret was - I went with a unicorn and my dad doesn't believe they are real.
Next, I built a giant sandcastle. It was as tall as me, kind of. We saw lots of people in deckchairs. My pet unicorn liked the waves and the rough sand on her hooves.

Finally, we saw lots of starfish and we collected them and put them on a couple of rocks.

Holly Graney (7)
Tynsel Parkes CE Primary Academy, Uttoxeter

Dear Diary

Yesterday I woke up excited because I was going to Alton Towers. I went with my mum, dad, sister and brother. We went on the monorail to get to the rides.

The first ride we went on was the river rapids. By the time we got off we were all soaking because of the water splashing us. Next, just me, my dad and my brother went on my favourite ride - 13! Me and my dad went at the front and my brother went behind. I was laughing a lot.

Then it was lunchtime and for lunch we went to Rollercoaster Restaurant. I had spaghetti Bolognese. It was yummy.

After that, we went on The Wicker Man. My dad was shouting so loud that he couldn't hear me saying, "Be quiet!"

Finally, we went to watch the fireworks. I had fries and hot chocolate. It was yummy. I had a fun time at Alton Towers.

Niamh Roberts (7)
Tynsel Parkes CE Primary Academy, Uttoxeter

Dear Diary

I went to the park on Monday and then afterwards I went to the theme park. I went on so many really cool rides. I went on a ride of the Ice Age. There was a really cool roller coaster. My mum said it was mega. I was so so happy. I had so much fun.

I had a burger when it came to dinner time and a big bottle of juice.

Next, we went on The Smiler. When my mum got off she was freaked out. I went on the new ride which bursts out freaky fire. Then I went into a dark oak tunnel. Then I went on a roller coaster that dropped me into a hole.

Then we went home and I had chips and nuggets for tea.

Evie Smithard (7)
Tynsel Parkes CE Primary Academy, Uttoxeter

Dear Diary

Yesterday I woke up and my dad told me that I was going to the beach. My dad told me that my friends were coming to the beach with us. I was so excited! I went in the car with my family, it took a long time. I played with friends and we played stuck in the mud in the sea and we swam in the sea. We went to the cafe, I had a big burger. My dad had an enormous burger.

We all went home and had a party because it was my birthday yesterday and I was seven. My dad bought me a pet unicorn, she was one year old. I rode my unicorn. I sang lullabies to my unicorn and we both fell asleep together.

Isla Ashby (7)

Tynsel Parkes CE Primary Academy, Uttoxeter

Dear Diary

Yesterday I went to Alton Towers. I went with Niamh, Daisy, Kaitlyn and my parents. It was my birthday so I chose the ride first. I chose Sea Life. I got to touch a starfish but no one else wanted to touch the starfish. After that, Niamh chose to go on the runaway mine train. It sounded like a train. I felt excited on it. It was fun. Then Daisy wanted to go on Hex. Hex was scary but we were brave. Kaitlyn wanted to go on Charlie and Lola.

We had lunch then we sang happy birthday. I then blew out all of the candles. It was a day I will never forget and it was a super day.

Elsie Gallimore (7)
Tynsel Parkes CE Primary Academy, Uttoxeter

Dear Diary

Yesterday I went to the zoo. I saw a giraffe, elephants, tigers, lions, rhino, monkeys and a leopard. When I went home I was singing in the car.

When I got home I had lunch. For lunch, I had a salad sandwich with sauce on, it was delicious. For pudding, I had a chocolate cake.

Then my sister and brothers got christened. I lit my candle because I had already been christened.

After, we had a family photo and then we went to the party. We had burgers, cake and a disco.

Layla Walley (7)
Tynsel Parkes CE Primary Academy, Uttoxeter

Dear Diary

I went to the park with Daisy, Niamh, Elsie and Isla. We played on the slide. Then we played ring-a-roses. Then we had dinner. I had pizza. We all shared it. After lunch, we went on the roller coaster and then went to the shops. I bought slime.
We went home and we had a sleepover. We had lots of candy. Daisy chose two films.
In the morning, we went to school. I love maths. I thought Niamh did the best. After school, I went to Elsie's house. We did slime. It was crunchy.

Kaitlyn Whitehead (7)
Tynsel Parkes CE Primary Academy, Uttoxeter

Dear Diary

Yesterday I went to the zoo. I saw lions, rhinos, monkeys and more. For lunch, I had macaroni and cheese. It was scrumptious. Then we watched the penguins go diving. Actually, when one was diving he hit his head on the glass above. After that, I saw a shop with a fluffy, soft toy penguin and my mum had to buy it for me.

Then I came back home and watched a movie called 'The Christmas Chronicles' and I snuggled in and went to bed with joy.

Kameel Malik (7)
Tynsel Parkes CE Primary Academy, Uttoxeter

Dear Diary

Yesterday I went to the funfair with an alien. I saw a dragon blowing fire. I was confused because I did not know that dragons were real.

Next, I went to the water slide. I saw Squirtle. He squirted water at me. Then I went to the empty field and I saw Caterpie and Tangler.

After that, I had a triple ice cream. I had chocolate sticks with all the ice cream.

Finally, I went home and had jacket potato, cheese and beans and chips.

Jacob Longmore (6)
Tynsel Parkes CE Primary Academy, Uttoxeter

Dear Diary

First, I went to the funfair and I went on the swings, the big slide, the helter-skelter and the dodgems. We had some pink candyfloss. Next, I rode on unicorns and we got to feed them some apples and carrots. They enjoyed the food.

After that, I went to the cafe and had a hot chocolate and a strawberry cake. It was delicious.

Then I went swimming and I swam to the bottom. It was fun!

Finally, we went home and went to bed.

Jenai Rose Flint (7)

Tynsel Parkes CE Primary Academy, Uttoxeter

Dear Diary

Yesterday I went to the Sea Life Centre. It was good because I saw seals, penguins, dolphins, starfish, crocodiles and killer whales. I went there to get a dragon, dinosaur, Pokémon and an animal. Guess what I got. An ice dragon, a deer, a new Pokémon and a raptor! When I got home I found out my ice dragon could do blue fire and red!

When it was night I saw the beautiful sunset and a shooting star! It was a great day!

Bethany Nicholls (6)
Tynsel Parkes CE Primary Academy, Uttoxeter

Dear Diary

Yesterday I went to a water park, the biggest one in the world and the most fun in the world. It has five pools - three are shallow and two are deep. It has twenty-five water slides. Five are 150cm, ten have a spiral in and ten are 200m tall. They were the biggest there in the whole water park. First, I went on a 180m spiral one. The water park came with 200 water pistols and 80 enormous water cannons in the park.

Harry Chatfield (7)
Tynsel Parkes CE Primary Academy, Uttoxeter

Dear Diary

Yesterday I went to the beach to play ping-pong, golf, tennis and go in the swimming pool. We also went to the kid paintball park and archery practise.

After that big day we went to the fair. There was a reptile centre and I bought a baby bearded dragon. It cost £100! I wasn't expecting that. It was a brilliant day in Scotland. It was the best day of my life.

Fletcher Hargreaves (6)

Tynsel Parkes CE Primary Academy, Uttoxeter

Dear Diary

Yesterday I went to the park. I went with my mum and my brother Owen. We played football and had a lot of fun. I scored twenty goals and Owen scored thirty. Then we had a party with my cousins. We ate sausages, crisps, chocolate cookies and chocolate whites. We played football and I scored some goals. I had a great day. In fact, I think it was the best day of my life.

Jackson Buxton (7)
Tynsel Parkes CE Primary Academy, Uttoxeter

Dear Diary

Yesterday I went to the park with a Pokémon. I went with Pikachu. We went on the swings, the slides and the roundabout. We played tig. I won seven rounds and Pikachu won six rounds. We had a picnic. I had a chicken sandwich and chips. Pikachu had electricity. We had lots of fun. After that, we had a play on my PS4. We had a good day!

Leon Furniss (7)
Tynsel Parkes CE Primary Academy, Uttoxeter

Dear Diary

Yesterday I went to the funfair with a unicorn. We went for tea but Isaac didn't like the cafe so we went to a pub. He liked that because the food was nicer than the cafe. I liked all of it! I played with my unicorn. We went on a roundabout but the unicorn didn't like it because she felt poorly.

Freya Bradley (6)

Tynsel Parkes CE Primary Academy, Uttoxeter

Dear Diary

Yesterday I went to the funfair with my unicorn pet, my family and my friends. We all went on the roller coaster and we went to go to get some cotton candy but my unicorn had rainbow sparkles cotton candy. Then we went to the place where you get strawberries and marshmallows with melted chocolate.

Hollie Ellerby (6)

Tynsel Parkes CE Primary Academy, Uttoxeter

Dear Diary

Yesterday I went to the park with a big dinosaur. The dinosaur was a T-rex. We played on the roundabout, swings, slides and the zip line. We had a picnic. I had a chicken burger with vegetables and chips. We had a race. I won. Then we went home and played outside. It was fun.

Corey Smith (7)
Tynsel Parkes CE Primary Academy, Uttoxeter

Dear Diary

Yesterday we went to the park with my brother and to the adventure farm to play in the play area. When I slid down the slide it was very fun. My brother was on another slide. Then I went to have some food inside. After that, I had a drink and it was good. Then we went home.

Riley Garner (7)

Tynsel Parkes CE Primary Academy, Uttoxeter

Dear Diary

Yesterday I went to Alton Towers. I went with Isra Thomas Peaty. We went on a roller coaster and we had a lot of fun. Next, we went on The Wicker Man and the haunted house. We went to a water park.

Isaac Smith (7)

Tynsel Parkes CE Primary Academy, Uttoxeter

Dear Diary

I went to the funfair with my friend Jenai. We had to ride on a unicorn to a swimming pool. We were in an enchanted forest. I saw an owl. We saw lots of animals.

Gracie May Jones (6)

Tynsel Parkes CE Primary Academy, Uttoxeter

Young Writers Information

We hope you have enjoyed reading this book – and that you will continue to in the coming years.

If you're a young writer who enjoys reading and creative writing, or the parent of an enthusiastic poet or story writer, do visit our website **www.youngwriters.co.uk**. Here you will find free competitions, workshops and games, as well as recommended reads, a poetry glossary and our blog. There's lots to keep budding writers motivated to write!

If you would like to order further copies of this book, or any of our other titles, then please give us a call or order via your online account.

Young Writers
Remus House
Coltsfoot Drive
Peterborough
PE2 9BF
(01733) 890066
info@youngwriters.co.uk

Join in the conversation!
Tips, news, giveaways and much more!

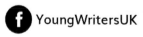 YoungWritersUK    @YoungWritersCW